Down by the Cool of the Pool

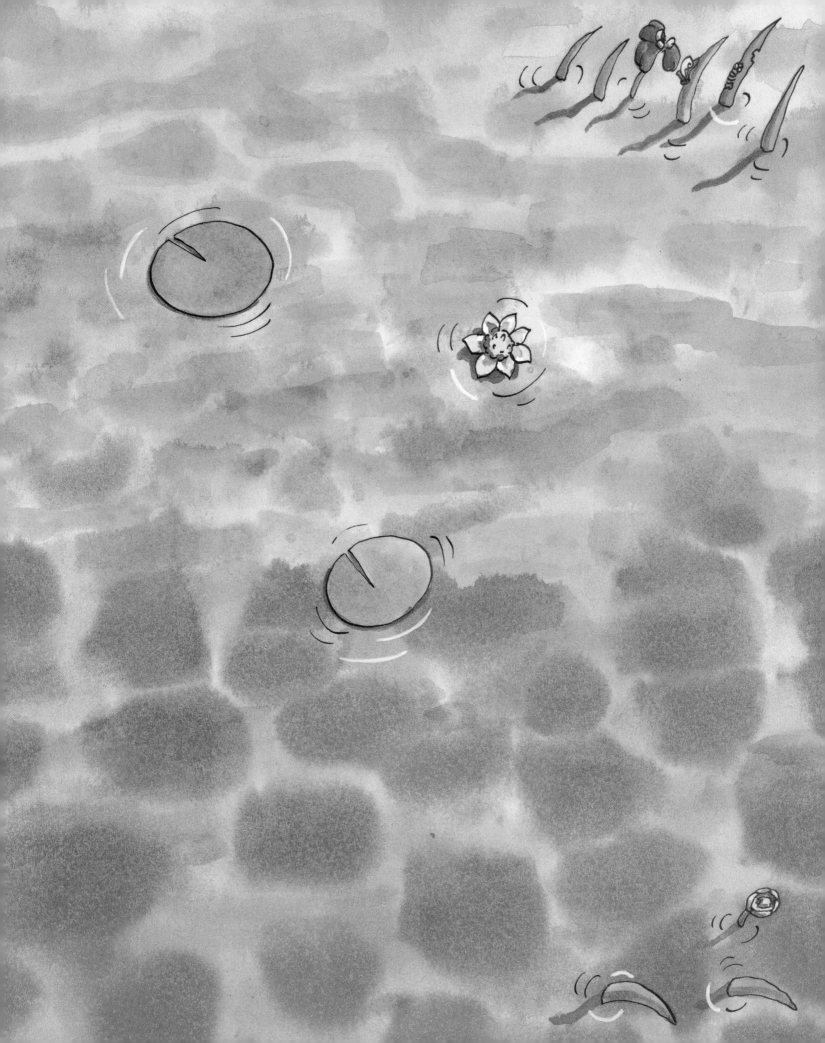

For George, Harriet, Doris and Guthrie,
and the cool of the pool in France – T.M.

For the lovely chucklesome little Joe – G.P-R.

ISBN 0-439-52476-8

30   10/0

Printed in the U.S.A.   40

First Scholastic printing, April 2003

Down by the Cool of the Pool

by Tony Mitton & illustrated by Guy Parker-Rees

SCHOLASTIC INC.

New York Toronto London Auckland Sydney
Mexico City New Delhi Hong Kong Buenos Aires

Down by the pool
in the cool of the day,
Frog cried, "**Wheeeee!**
Can you dance like me?"

Duck came to see.

"I can dance too.

But not like you.

I can flap."

So Duck went "flap,"

and Frog cried,

"Wheeeee!

Can you dance like me?"

Down by the cool of the pool.

Pig came to see.
"I can dance too. But not like you.
I can "**wiggle**.""

So Pig went "**wiggle**",

Duck went "**flap**",

Sheep came to see.
"I can dance too.
But not like you.
I can stamp."

So Sheep went

Stamp,

Then up sprang Cat with a sudden **bound,**

and Dog came "frisking" round and round.

Goat butted in with a **skip** and a **hop**, and Frog cried, "**Wheeeee!** That's great! Don't stop."

Then Playful Pony began to **prance**, and Donkey **drummed** his hoofbeat dance.

With a **stamp**, and a **"wiggle"**,

and a "**WhOOPS!**
Watch out !"
and a **tOPPle**", and a ...

But did they stop?

We're having fun, dancing our dance **in** the cool of the pool!"

And they **splished** and **splashed** till their dance was done.

Then away they drifted,

and down went the sun,

as there by the cool
of the ripply pool

with a hop hop

PLOP!

even Frog . . .
was gone.

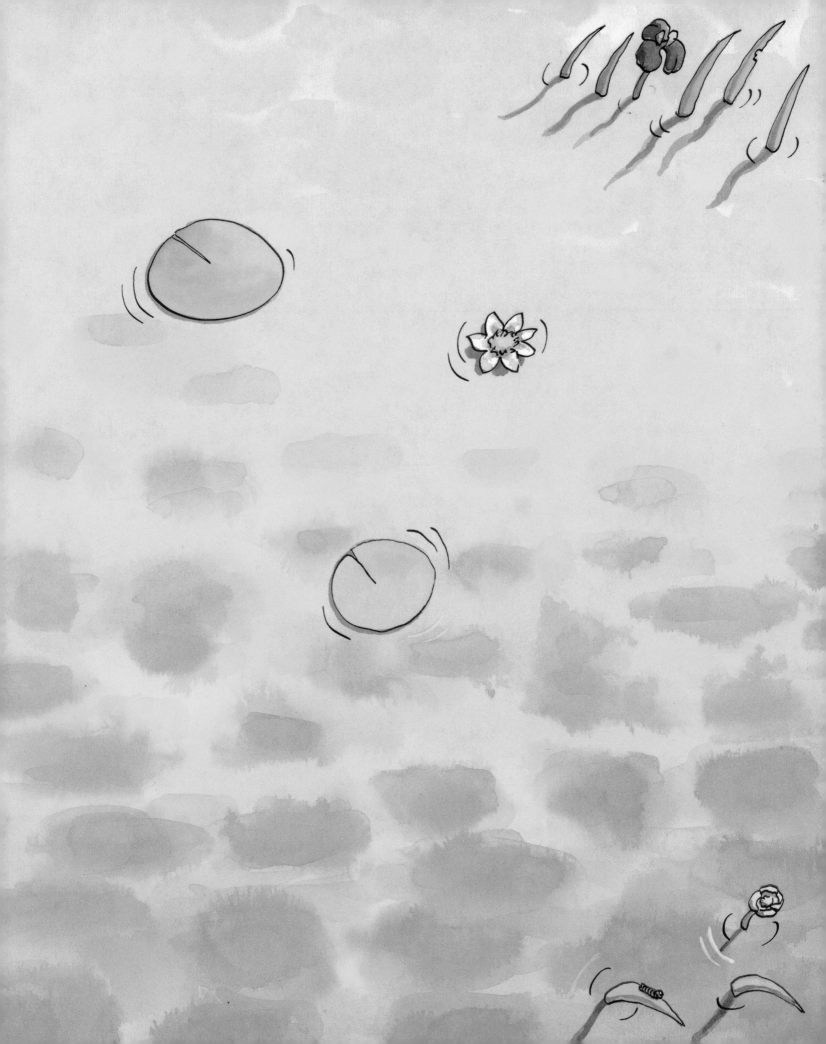